TRANSFORM YOURSELF, TRANSFORM YOUR BUSINESS

TRANSFORM YOURSELF, TRANSFORM YOUR BUSINESS
A 30-DAY JOURNAL OF SELF-EXPLORATION AND EMPOWERMENT

CREATED BY MELISSA ZAVALA

A Division of Melrose Publications
San Diego
2016

www.melrosepublications.com

ISBN 978-0-9860526-7-5

Printed in the United States of America

Book Design by Explore that Store

Photo Source: iStock by Getty Images

For real estate agents everywhere

INTRODUCTION

When I came across Henry Ford's quote (the first one in this journal), I could really relate. Throughout my real estate career, I have always been somewhat aware of the competition. Ford said, "The competitor to be feared is one who never bothers about you at all, but goes on making his own business better all the time."

As real estate professionals, we are always looking for new and exciting ways to build our business. In fact, sometimes there are so many things going on (between representing buyers and sellers, generating leads and prospecting), that those new ideas are often fleeting.

In addition to your Pipeline Planner, wouldn't it be great to have a place where you could sit and jot down ideas about your own business?

The 30 motivational quotes in this short journal have been selected exclusively to give you the inspiration you need to make your own business better and be the best that you can be.

As you read the famous inspirational words on these pages, reflect on your own business and your own life. Consider ways to improve your business, to improve yourself, and to be the best that you can be. Explore the thoughts and feelings surrounding your own life, and use the space provided for journaling—for both transformational thinking and self-exploration.

Enjoy!

Melissa Zavala

"THE COMPETITOR TO BE FEARED IS ONE WHO NEVER BOTHERS ABOUT YOU AT ALL, BUT GOES ON MAKING HIS OWN BUSINESS BETTER ALL THE TIME."

— HENRY FORD

"YOU DON'T HAVE TO BE GREAT TO START,
BUT YOU HAVE TO START TO BE GREAT."

— ZIG ZIGLAR

PIPE
LINE
PRODUCTS

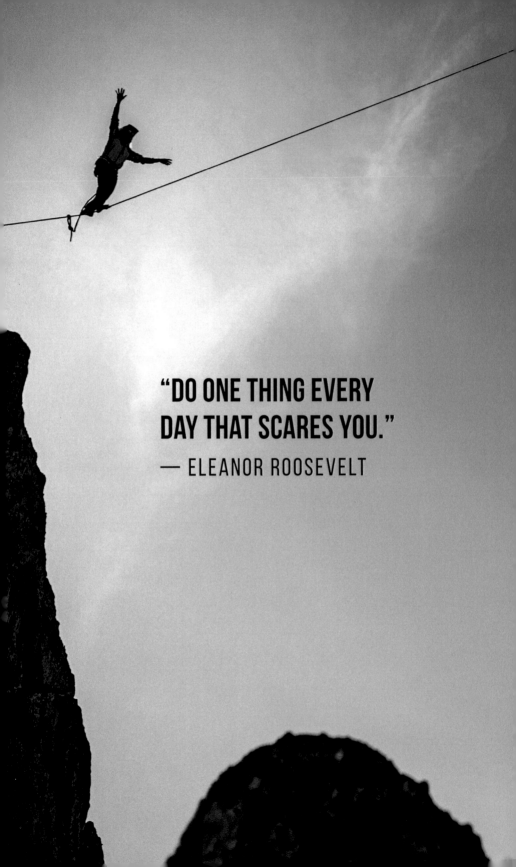

"DO ONE THING EVERY
DAY THAT SCARES YOU."

— ELEANOR ROOSEVELT

"YOU CAN EITHER FIT IN
OR STAND OUT. NOT BOTH."

— SETH GODIN

"WHAT SEEMS TO US AS BITTER TRIALS ARE OFTEN BLESSINGS IN DISGUISE."

— OSCAR WILDE

"HOW WE SPEND OUR DAYS IS, OF
COURSE, HOW WE SPEND OUR LIVES."

— ANNIE DILLARD

"EITHER YOU RUN THE DAY
OR THE DAY RUNS YOU."

— JIM ROHN

"PREPARATION, I HAVE OFTEN SAID, IS RIGHTLY TWO-THIRDS OF ANY VENTURE."

— AMELIA EARHART

PIPE
LINE
PRODUCTS

"IT'S NOT ENOUGH TO BE BUSY.
SO ARE THE ANTS. THE QUESTION IS:
WHAT ARE WE BUSY ABOUT?"

— HENRY DAVID THOREAU

PIPE
LINE
PRODUCTS

"INSANITY: DOING THE SAME THING OVER AND OVER AND EXPECTING DIFFERENT RESULTS."

— ALBERT EINSTEIN

TRANSFORM YOURSELF, TRANSFORM YOUR BUSINESS : A 30-DAY JOURNAL OF SELF-EXPLORATION AND EMPOWERMENT

"TAKE THE FIRST STEP IN FAITH. YOU DON'T HAVE TO SEE THE WHOLE STAIRCASE, JUST TAKE THE FIRST STEP."

— MARTIN LUTHER KING, JR.

"EVERY SUCCESS STORY IS A
TALE OF CONSTANT ADAPTATION,
REVISION, AND CHANGE."

— SIR RICHARD BRANSON

"IT ISN'T WHAT WE SAY OR THINK THAT DEFINES US, BUT WHAT WE DO."

— JANE AUSTEN

"IN THE BUSINESS WORLD, THE REARVIEW MIRROR IS ALWAYS CLEARER THAN THE WINDSHIELD."

— WARREN BUFFETT

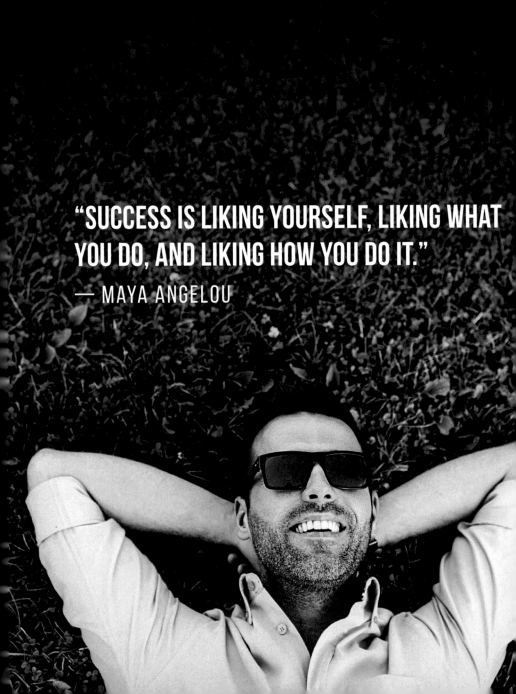

"SUCCESS IS LIKING YOURSELF, LIKING WHAT YOU DO, AND LIKING HOW YOU DO IT."

— MAYA ANGELOU

"NO MATTER WHO YOU ARE, NO MATTER
WHAT YOU DID, NO MATTER WHERE YOU'VE
COME FROM, YOU CAN ALWAYS CHANGE,
BECOME A BETTER VERSION OF YOURSELF."

— MADONNA

PIPE
LINE
PRODUCTS

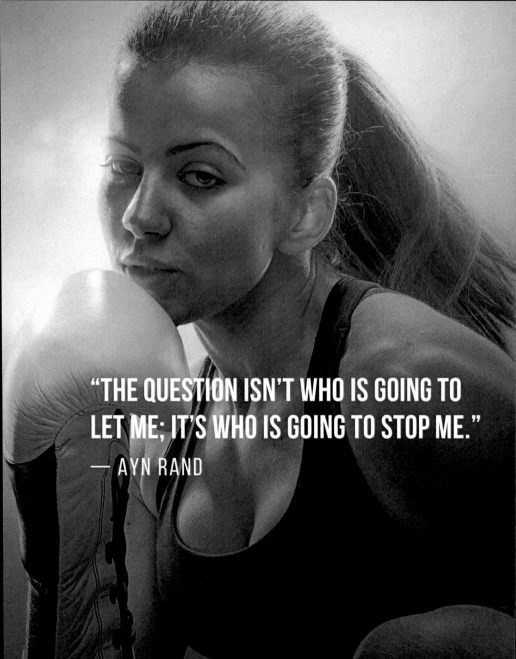

"THE QUESTION ISN'T WHO IS GOING TO LET ME; IT'S WHO IS GOING TO STOP ME."

— AYN RAND

PIPE
LINE
PRODUCTS

"DON'T TELL ME THE SKY'S THE LIMIT WHEN THERE ARE FOOTPRINTS ON THE MOON."

— PAUL BRANDT

PIPE
LINE
PRODUCTS

"THERE ARE NO MISTAKES,
ONLY OPPORTUNITIES."

— TINA FEY

"WHY WORRY? IF YOU'VE DONE THE VERY BEST YOU CAN, WORRYING WON'T MAKE IT ANY BETTER."

— WALT DISNEY

"THE BIGGEST ADVENTURE YOU CAN TAKE
IS TO LIVE THE LIFE OF YOUR DREAMS."

— OPRAH WINFREY

"YESTERDAY'S HOME RUNS
DON'T WIN TODAY'S GAMES."

— BABE RUTH

PIPE
LINE
PRODUCTS

"IF IT'S YOUR JOB TO EAT A FROG, IT'S BEST TO DO IT FIRST THING IN THE MORNING. AND IF IT'S YOUR JOB TO EAT TWO FROGS, IT'S BEST TO EAT THE BIGGEST ONE FIRST."

— MARK TWAIN

PIPE
LINE
PRODUCTS

"PERSEVERANCE IS FAILING 19
TIMES AND SUCCEEDING THE 20TH."

— JULIE ANDREWS

PIPE
LINE
PRODUCTS

"BE LIKE A DUCK. REMAIN CALM ON THE SURFAC
AND PADDLE LIKE HELL UNDERNEATH."

— MICHAEL CAINE

"COURAGE DOESN'T ALWAYS ROAR. SOMETIMES COURAGE IS THE QUIET VOICE AT THE END OF THE DAY SAYING, 'I WILL TRY AGAIN TOMORROW.'"

— MARY ANNE RADMACHER

PIPE
LINE
PRODUCTS

"TRUST YOUR GUT, YOU KNOW MORE THAN YOU THINK YOU KNOW."

— DR. SPOCK

"WHAT LIES BEHIND US AND WHAT
LIES BEFORE US ARE TINY MATTERS
COMPARED TO WHAT LIES WITHIN US."

— RALPH WALDO EMERSON

"BE SO GOOD THEY CAN'T IGNORE YOU."
— STEVE MARTIN

"THERE ARE NO SECRETS TO SUCCESS.
IT IS THE RESULT OF PREPARATION,
HARD WORK, LEARNING FROM FAILURE."

— COLIN POWELL

Made in the USA
San Bernardino, CA
20 November 2016